NEW DAY

Name

....

....

Made in the USA
Monee, IL
02 June 2022

97379711R00065